Food Fight

by Carol Pugliano-Martin
illustrated by Claire Louise Milne

Table of Contents

Chapter 1

At the End of the Day

"Whew! Am I ever glad this day is over!"

Leo and Sam were closing up Leo's grocery store for the night. They had just finished putting fallen items back on the shelves and mopping the floors. Leo was counting the money from the day's sales.

"Yeah, it sure was busy," said Leo. "Well, weekends usually are."

"I think I'll give these apples one last polish," said Sam. "We want them to look their best when we open tomorrow."

Sam walked to the front of the store where the apples and the rest of the produce were.

"You guys are lucky," Sam said. "It must be nice and quiet here in the store at night."

"Sam, you must be working too hard if you're talking to apples!" Leo laughed.

Sam took out a cloth and began to vigorously polish the apples to a beautiful sheen. As he finished each apple, he placed it carefully back in its place in the neatly stacked pile.

Leo finished methodically counting the day's money and placed it carefully in an envelope to take to the bank.

"You know, you're right, Sam," said Leo. "It probably is peaceful here. When I get home, it's chaotic. Getting the kids in the tub, getting them ready for bed. It's go, go, go! Maybe some day for a break, I'll sleep in the store. I certainly could use some peace and quiet."

"Sounds like a great idea!" laughed Sam appreciatively as he shined the last apple. "There now, you apples look great. I can see myself in your beautiful red skin."

"Good job, Sam. Come on, let's lock up," Leo said as he took out the key to the store's front door. He turned off several switches and the store grew dark. "See you tomorrow, groceries. Don't get into any trouble while we're gone."

Leo and Sam both laughed as Leo locked the doors behind them.

Chapter 2

Disgruntled Dairy

The store was dark, but it was certainly not peaceful. In the back of the store, way in the back, a carton of milk was not pleased.

"Did you see those apples getting their special polish?" shouted the milk. "Who do they think they are?"

Next to the milk were the yogurt, butter, and cheese. They were all in the refrigerated dairy case.

"We've been through this before, Milk," said the yogurt. "The apples and all the produce get special treatment because they are in the front of the store."

"It's how a lot of stores are, Milk," the butter said. "It's just traditional to have the produce in the front and the dairy in the back. It's been that way here since the founding of the store."

"Well I'm tired of it," said the milk. "I feel like an outcast, banished to the back, and I'm going to do something about it."

The yogurt looked positively confused. "But what can you do?" she asked.

"I have a plan," said the milk determinedly. "We're moving up front."

The yogurt looked extremely worried, but the butter looked excited. The cheese looked adoringly at the milk since they were an item.

"Well, count me out," said the yogurt. "I'm too cultured to take such risks."

The cheese had been quiet all along, but finally she spoke up. "I'll support you, honey," said the cheese. The milk smiled at her in appreciation.

"OK, here's the plan," began the milk. "We're tired of being in the back, right?"

"Right!" agreed the butter and the cheese.

"We want to be in front, where we are the first items the customers see, right?" asked the milk, his voice rising.

"Right!" echoed the butter and cheese, who were also getting louder.

With a glance at the yogurt, the milk then discreetly whispered his complex strategy to the other dairy items.

Chapter 3

The Produce Fights Back

Meanwhile, at the front of the store, the word of the dairy's plan had spread through the grapevine. In fact, it was the grapes who told the rest of the produce what was going on.

"They're moving in on us, fellas," said the grapes ominously. "What are we going to do?"

"We can't let it happen!" said an apple defensively. "We're up front for a reason. Look how good we look!"

"It's absolutely true we do," said the head apple. "I glisten like a brand-new car. We all do! And we certainly deserve to be seen first!"

"Yes, but that dairy group is pretty strong," said the oranges. "Especially the milk."

The head apple looked unimpressed. "Well, I have a plan to stop their madness. Let's get the other produce involved. We need all the help we can get. Hey, you grapes, thanks bunches for the information."

"Any time," said the grapes.

The apples began to enlist the help of the other fruits and vegetables.

"We're all ears!" said the corn when the apples told them the story.

"We can be the lookouts," said the potatoes. "We have eyes in the backs of our heads!"

So the produce started devising their plan, and soon they were ready.

Back in the dairy case, the milk finished revealing his plan.

"The only way to get the recognition we deserve is to compete with the produce for attention," said the milk.

"I'm with you, Boss. We must be the first things the customers see," said the butter. "We're just as good-looking as that old produce."

"Hey, who are you calling old?" It was a carrot who had hopped his way to the back of the store and was eavesdropping on the dairy's plan. "We're fresh as fresh can be!"

"Listen, Carrot-top, get back to your stack," snapped the milk.

The carrot tried bravely to stand up to the milk. He had been sent by the others to gather important information. But he was inexperienced and afraid, so he quickly hopped back to the produce section.

Suddenly a shopping cart pulled up in front of the dairy case.

"Ah, my chariot awaits!" said the milk. "OK, Cart, you know the drill. You'll drive us up to the front and wait, right?"

"Right," said the cart. "As long as you don't forget your promise."

"I absolutely will not because I'm a milk of my word," said the milk. "The deal is my friend here, the butter, will grease your squeaky wheels. Isn't that correct, Butter?"

"Yes, sir!" said the butter.

"Well, let's get the show on the road!" said the milk.

Some packages of cheese, including the milk's lady friend, formed a ramp. The butter pushed the milk down the ramp and into the cart. He wobbled a bit, but quickly righted himself. The butter followed him and found a secure spot in the cart as well.

The milk held his head high. "To the front!" he shouted as the cart began to zoom down the aisle.

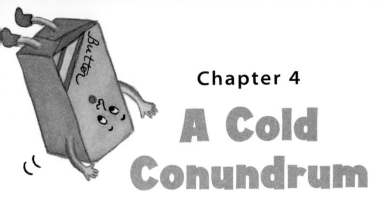

Chapter 4

A Cold Conundrum

The cart zipped down the aisle at breakneck speed. The milk and the butter held on for dear life. As the cart passed shelf after shelf, some items began cheering enthusiastically.

"Go! Go!" shouted the pasta. They were quite fond of the dairy items.

Other items began jeering menacingly.

"Hey, stay where you belong," yelled the cookies. They had always had a fear of being dunked in milk and were against the dairy's plan.

The cart zoomed speedily on.

Back at the produce section, the fruit and vegetables were ready.

"OK, now!" shouted the head apple authoritatively.

Suddenly ears of corn hurled themselves recklessly off their shelf and rolled under the cart's wheels. The cart swerved to get out of the way, but still it kept going.

"We're under attack!" shouted the butter nervously.

"Now!" shouted the apple again.

Some potatoes rolled in front of the cart, causing it to swerve again, this time toppling some cereal. It was bedlam! Still, the cart kept going.

The oranges uniformly rolled off their pile and in front of the cart.

The cart slammed on its brakes and came to a screeching halt. But it had reached the front of the store, successfully foiling the produce's plan.

The milk and butter were triumphant, but their joy was short-lived.

"Ah, victory!" shouted the milk exuberantly.

"Um . . . Boss . . . there's just one problem," said the butter cautiously.

"Problem? But we've won!" said the milk.

"But, it's not cold enough up here, and we'll go bad," said the butter, defeated.

"Cold? Drats!" said the milk. "Hey, look over there. The specialty juices have got their own private refrigerator. Surely they'll let us in!"

"Sorry, but there's a space shortage," said the leader of the juice. "Besides, we're loyal to the produce because, after all, we're juice and juice is made from fruit and vegetables."

Chapter 5
The Tradition Continues

The milk and the butter hung their heads. They had come so far, and now they had failed. What would the others think back in the dairy case?

"It's over, Butter," said the milk. "I can't believe I forgot about refrigeration."

"Don't you worry, Boss. You had a dream and you went for it. Here's a reassuring pat," said the butter.

The milk sighed and said, "Well, Cart, if you've got any energy left, please return us to the dairy case."

The ride back to the dairy case was much slower than the breakneck ride to the front.

"Hey, no hard feelings, OK?" said the apple.

"No, none," said the milk.

When the cart got back to the dairy case, the cheese formed the ramp to help the milk and the butter get to the shelf.

"I promise I won't say that I told you so," said the yogurt. "But things are the way they are for a reason. Civilization as we know it has the produce up front and the dairy in the back. The customers have come to rely on that. It's one of the few things in this crazy world they can count on."

"I suppose you're right," said the milk contemplatively. "I've had time to reflect on the ride back up here, and I realize now that it's not important to be seen first. As long as we're seen, you know?"

In the aisle where the cart had zoomed, several mice were talking amongst the rubble.

"Oh, we're definitely going to be blamed for this!" said one mouse.

"As usual," said the other mice, in unison.

The sun was beginning to come up as Leo turned his key in the lock. Another grocery day had begun.

Comprehension Check

Summarize

What is the theme of this story? How do the actions of Milk support the theme? Use a Theme Chart to help you organize your ideas.

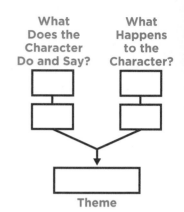

What Does the Character Do and Say?

What Happens to the Character?

Theme

Think and Compare

1. Both the produce and the dairy have reasons for the actions they take in this story. List the reasons they have for fighting for what they believe in. *(Theme)*

2. The milk says he feels like an outcast. Have you ever felt like an outcast? If so, did you overcome that feeling? How? *(Evaluate)*

3. The yogurt explains that people rely on the tradition of the produce being in the front and the dairy being in the back of the store. What other traditions do you think people have come to rely on? Tell why you think traditions are important. *(Analyze/Evaluate)*